They're Playing Your Song, Charlie Brown

Selected cartoons from
WIN A FEW, LOSE A FEW,
CHARLIE BROWN, Vol. 2

Charles M. Schulz

CORONET BOOKS
Hodder Fawcett, London

Copyright © 1973, 1974 by United
Feature Syndicate, Inc.

First published by Fawcett Publications
Inc., New York

Coronet edition 1979

Printed in Great Britain for Hodder
Fawcett Ltd., Mill Road, Dunton Green,
Sevenoaks, Kent (Editorial Office: 47
Bedford Square, London, WC1 3DP) by
C. Nicholls & Company Ltd.,
The Philips Park Press, Manchester

ISBN 0 340 23839 9

THEY'RE PLAYING YOUR SONG, CHARLIE BROWN

WHERE ARE YOU GOING IN SUCH A HURRY?

SNOWMAN PRACTICE! I'M ON THE "SILVER FLAKES," AND WE PRACTICE EVERY TUESDAY...IF I'M LATE, THE COACH WILL KILL ME!

YOU'D BETTER GET ON A TEAM, BIG BROTHER...YOU CAN'T BUILD A SNOWMAN ANY MORE UNLESS YOU'RE ON A TEAM!

GO, SILVER FLAKES!

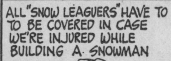

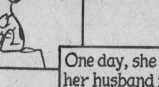

They had named their Great Dane "Good Authority."

One day, she asked her husband if he had seen her new belt.

"Belt?" he said. "Oh, I'm sorry. I thought it was a dog collar. I have it on Good Authority."

Shortly thereafter, their marriage began to go downhill.

Schulz

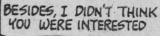

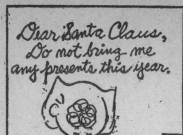

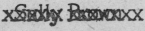

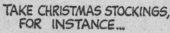

HERE WE ARE SKATING OUT ONTO WOODSTOCK'S HOME ICE FOR THE BIG HOCKEY GAME...

AND HERE COME THE OFFICIALS...

THE REFEREE

Winter had come again all too soon, and it was time for Joe Jacket to bring in his polar cows.

As he rode out from the barn, the first flakes of snow began to fall.

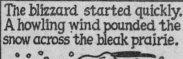

The Monster and the Bunnies

A Tale of Terror and Suspense

"Boo!" said the Monster.

WOW!!

Science Report:
The comet, Kohoutek,
went around the sun
a week ago.

DON'T FORGET THE PART
ABOUT THE WORLD
COMING TO AN END....

Some ignorant creatures
think this is a sign
that the world is
coming to an end.

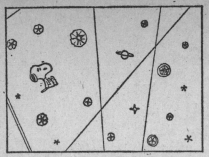

➡

NO, LET'S PUT IT ON THAT TABLE BACK THERE... HOW ABOUT YOU FOUR WEIRDOS MOVING THAT TABLE?

AND I'LL NEED A COUPLE MORE TO PUT THIS SCREEN UP... LET'S GO!! ON THE DOUBLE, THERE!

STRETCH THAT CORD ACROSS THE BACK, AND PLUG IT INTO THAT SOCKET IN THE CORNER...

OKAY, SOMEONE RUN DOWN TO THE CUSTODIAN THEN, AND GET AN EXTENSION! YOU THERE, GET GOING!!

NOW, WHAT ABOUT THOSE WINDOW SHADES? LET'S HAVE ALL OF YOU WHO SIT ALONG THE SIDE THERE PULL DOWN THOSE STUPID SHADES..

AND I'LL NEED SOMEONE ON THE LIGHT SWITCH... ONE VOLUNTEER... YOU THERE, HONEY, GET THE SWITCH!

IS THAT THE BELL ALREADY?

OKAY, WE'LL TAKE IT TOMORROW FROM HERE.. EVERYONE BE IN PLACE BY NINE! THANK YOU, AND GOOD MORNING!

SCHULZ

➤→

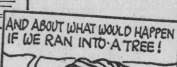

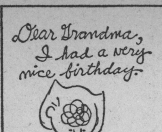

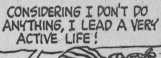

➤

"WHO WAS THE PILOT OF THE PLANE THAT TOOK RONALD COLMAN TO SHANGRI-LA IN 'LOST HORIZON'?"

GOOD GRIEF!

I SHOULD KNOW BETTER THAN TO PLAY "TRIVIA" WITH WOODSTOCK!

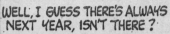

SOMETIMES I THINK YOU DON'T REALIZE THAT YOU COULD LOSE ME...

ARE YOU SURE YOU WANT TO SUFFER THE TORTURES OF THE MEMORY OF A LOST LOVE?

DO YOU KNOW THE TORTURES OF THE MEMORY OF A LOST LOVE?

SIR, PLEASE COME DOWN, AND LET'S GO TO SCHOOL...

IF WE HURRY, WE CAN STILL MAKE IT TO SECOND PERIOD...

I HATE SECOND PERIOD! BESIDES, I'VE ALREADY TOLD YOU I'M GOING TO SIT HERE WITH SNOOPY FOR THE REST OF MY LIFE!

WE'RE JUST GOING TO SIT HERE AND BEEP EACH OTHER ON THE NOSE..... BEEP!!

THRILLSVILLE '74!

SIR, YOU'RE BEING VERY FOOLISH!

I'M LOSING MY PATIENCE WITH YOU, SIR! WE HAVE TO GO TO SCHOOL!!

COME DOWN FROM THERE RIGHT NOW, AND LET'S GO TO SCHOOL!!!!

MARCIE, HAS ANYONE EVER TOLD YOU THAT WHEN YOU'RE MAD, YOU LOOK JUST LIKE BILLIE JEAN KING?

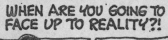

ALSO AVAILABLE FROM CORONET BOOKS

CHARLES M. SCHULZ

☐	22307 3	Snoopy And His Sopwith Camel	75p
☐	23236 6	You've Asked For It Charlie Brown	60p
☐	22951 9	Play Ball Snoopy	60p
☐	22778 8	It's Your Turn Snoopy	60p
☐	22304 9	That's Life Snoopy	60p
☐	21983 1	You've Got To Be You, Snoopy	60p
☐	21797 9	Watch Out Charlie Brown	60p

JOHNNY HART & BRANT PARKER

☐	15816 6	The King's A Fink	60p
☐	19815 X	The Wizard's Back	60p
☐	23017 7	Wizard Of Id Let There Be Reign	60p

PARKER/RECHIN/WILDER

☐	23230 7	Crock	60p

All these books are available at your local bookshop or newsagent, or can be ordered direct from the publisher. Just tick the titles you want and fill in the form below.

Prices and availability subject to change without notice.

〰〰〰〰〰〰〰〰〰〰〰〰〰〰〰〰〰〰〰〰〰〰〰〰〰〰〰

CORONET BOOKS, P.O. Box 11, Falmouth, Cornwall.
Please send cheque or postal order, and allow the following for postage and packing:

U.K. – One book 22p plus 10p per copy for each additional book ordered, up to a maximum of 82p.

B.F.P.O. and EIRE – 22p for the first book plus 10p per copy for the next 6 books, thereafter 4p per book.

OTHER OVERSEAS CUSTOMERS – 30p for the first book and 10p per copy for each additional book.

Name ....

Address ....

....